MAD MOOSE'S PERPLEXING PICTURE PUZZLES

Managing Editors: Simon Melhuish and Emma Craven
Series Editor: Nikole G Bamford
Puzzle Compilers: Dilemma Puzzles
Cover Design and Moose Illustrations: Alan Shiner

Published by:
MAD MOOSE PRESS
UNIT 1
10 BECTIVE PLACE
LONDON
SW15 2PZ

ISBN: 1-904139-03-5

Printed in Great Britain

MAD MOOSE'S PERPLEXING PICTURE PUZZLES

MAD MOOSE'S PERPLEXING PICTURE PUZZLES

Another title in the series:

MAD MOOSE'S WICKED WORDSEARCHES
ISBN 1-904139-02-7

Welcome to the puzzling world of

Mad Moose.

There's nothing Mad Moose likes better
than to solve a puzzle or two. Here he
has selected over 170 picture puzzles for
you to enjoy. Get an eyeful of these odd
ones out and spot the differences,
mazes, blockbusters and battleships. So
for the best in visual delight sit back, pick
up a pen and puzzle.

FISHY

Which two fish are identical?

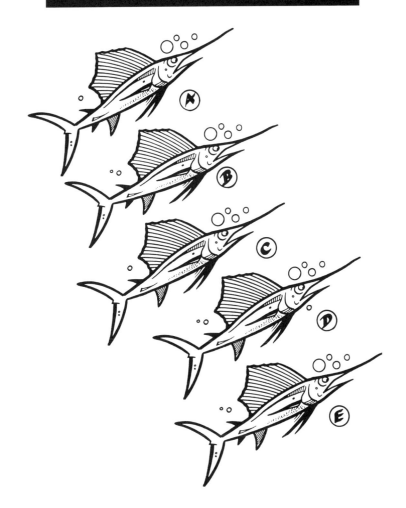

ODD SPACE

Which astronaut is the odd one out?

SHADOW PLAY

Which is the karate kid's shadow?

TWIN PLANETS

Which two planets are identical?

LOOKS FISHY

Which picture is the odd one out?

TREES & TENTS

*These tree and tent puzzles are straightforward to do,
just by following a few simple rules. Firstly, each tree in the grid
supports one tent, which must be in an adjacent square to the tree, to the
left, right, up or down, but not diagonally. In addition, no tent may be
adjacent to any other tent, either horizontally, vertically or diagonally.
The numbers along the rows and columns of the grid indicate the
number of tents in that row or column.*

	2	2	2	1	3	2	2	2	1	3
3			🌳						🌳	
2						🌳				
2		🌳		🌳						🌳
2							🌳			
2	🌳			🌳						🌳
1								🌳		
3		🌳		🌳		🌳			🌳	
1										
3	⛺		🌳				🌳			
1	🌳			🌳					🌳	

BLACK CROW

Which silhouette exactly
matches the picture of the scarecrow?

WHICH PAPER?

Mr. Dingle needs two more rolls of wallpaper to match the one he already has. Which two are they?

ALIENATED!

Which alien is the odd one out?

Can you spot 10 differences in the bottom picture?

PLANT POSER

Which silhouette matches the plant?

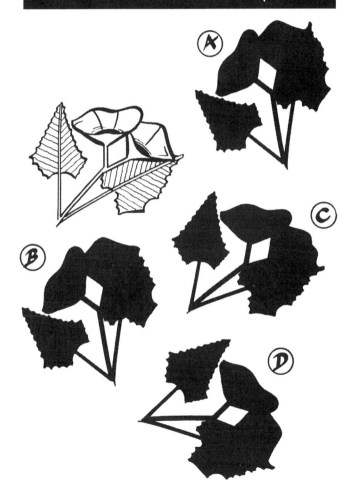

BALLOONY

Which two balloons are identical?

NEWS ITEM

Which TV newsreader is the odd one out?

See if you can spot 8 differences in the bottom picture.

BLAST OFF

Which silhouette exactly matches
the original picture of the rocket?

STORMWATCH

Storm clouds are gathering -
but which two are identical?

BLOCKBUSTER

To solve these Blockbuster puzzles, just follow a few simple rules:

Hidden in the grid is a picture, made up of dark squares and blank spaces. The numbers beside each row and column refer to the distinct blocks of dark squares in that row or column, each block separated from the next one by at least one blank space. As an example, '4,5,2' would indicate that, from left to right, there is a block of 4 dark squares, followed by at least one blank, then a block of 5, and finally a block of 2.

While you may not be able to say for definite where these blocks start and finish, you can often look at all the possibilities and fill in some squares that will always definitely be dark. It's also a good idea to mark squares that can only be blank with a small dot.

By constantly cross-referencing rows and columns, the picture should start to come together, as you fill in more dark squares and blank spaces. There should be no guessing or ambiguities - these puzzles have only one perfect solution!

Try this first puzzle for size, and you should get an idea of how the more complex puzzles later on work - some of them even include a couple of 'starter' squares to give you a helping hand.

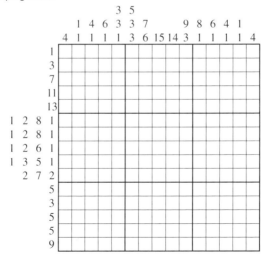

WORDSEARCH

We have hidden 15 different items, each beginning
with the letter 'M' in the box of letters. Can you find
them all in less than ten minutes?

```
G Z X H F I F O C V Y L
J S S H D B E J Q L T A
E P D B Y L U E N Q X D
W D I P M L P T A D A E
Z S M Q M O O N V I Y M
K Z X K U O S M S A F Y
C L F S M M F Q X M W L
J A J A C M P F U R R C
H D Z M D M A G N E T D
M Q N Y P O I P Y M N T
A M I C R O P H O N E W
D A A X B S A O J L U W
B T T M U E R B L I G G
O A N N M H G A A Y B N
D D U E S O M B D D H J
T O O U U D T C S K E P
K R M Z L U Y H O C L C
M R L R O B A P T G K S
```

PAIR OF WINGS

Which two butterflies are identical?

Spot 8 differences in the bottom picture.

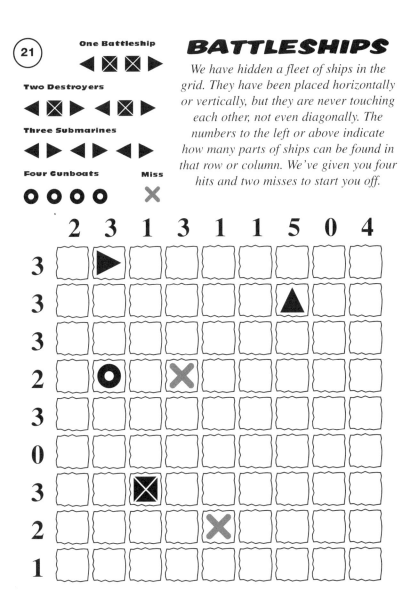

(21)

One Battleship

Two Destroyers

Three Submarines

Four Gunboats   **Miss**

BATTLESHIPS

We have hidden a fleet of ships in the grid. They have been placed horizontally or vertically, but they are never touching each other, not even diagonally. The numbers to the left or above indicate how many parts of ships can be found in that row or column. We've given you four hits and two misses to start you off.

Which silhouette matches the
picture of the cockatiel?

HATS OFF

Which hat matches the one this lady is wearing?

BREAD SPREAD

Shade in the dotted areas to reveal this lady's favourite topping!

WORDSEARCH

(25)

We have hidden 15 different items, each beginning with the letter 'F' in the box of letters. Can you find them all in less than ten minutes?

```
H W U E Y P Q D B G V F
H F C I O U B L T F Z J
H P H G J F U S E I F D
K I T C Q C I D N R R U
K J I Y A H O S F E Z K
B U I U P R K A H M V H
W M F T A L W T M A N Q
H M N S S T A H K N T U
Q F L O W E R U P H H N
K X E I F L A M I N G O
W Q N N F O U N T A I N
A S N L C N R Y S O L Y
E A U N A E Y T F P H A
P Q F Y G Q A R B L S M
D J G N E U O E O A A U
U D I Y Z G G Z F Z L G
S F B J Z R F E I W F L
X K R O W E R I F Z X G
```

LOCH NESS TEST

Which Loch Ness monster is the odd one out?

SPOT the DIFFERENCE

Can you spot 6 differences in the bottom picture?

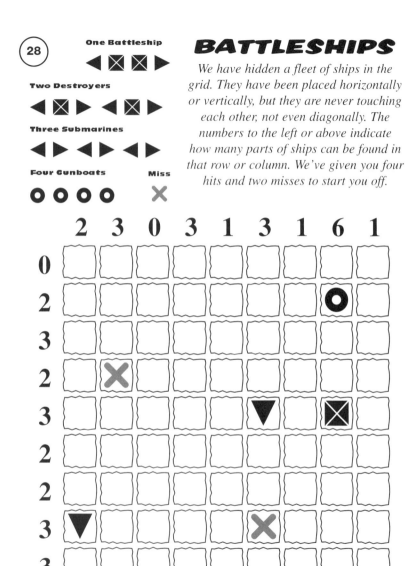

One Battleship

Two Destroyers

Three Submarines

Four Gunboats   **Miss**

BATTLESHIPS

We have hidden a fleet of ships in the grid. They have been placed horizontally or vertically, but they are never touching each other, not even diagonally. The numbers to the left or above indicate how many parts of ships can be found in that row or column. We've given you four hits and two misses to start you off.

	2	3	0	3	1	3	1	6	1
0									
2								O	
3									
2		X							
3						▼		X	
2									
2									
3	▼					X			
3									

SHADOW BOXER

Which is the boxer's shadow?

BATTY

Which two bats are identical?

NAME GAME

Shade in the dotted areas to reveal this man's name.

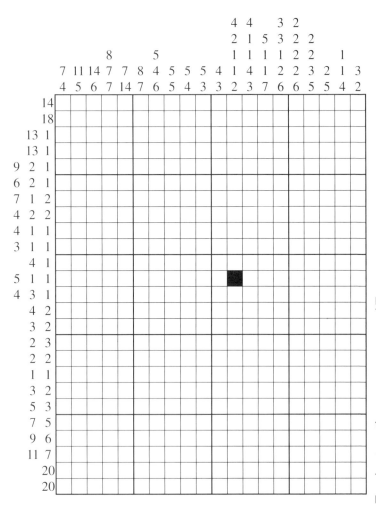

For instructions, see page 17

RHINO RIDDLE

Which rhinoceros is the odd one out?

Can you spot 6 differences in the bottom picture?

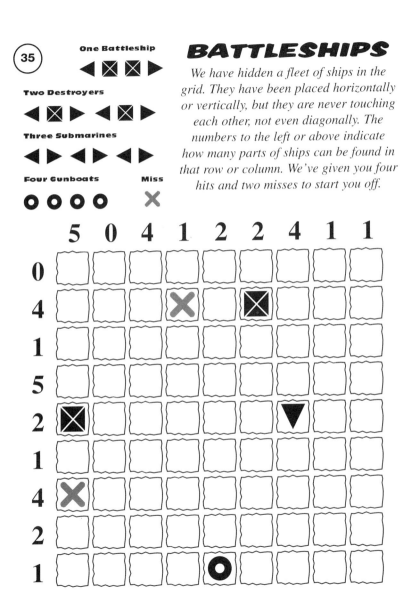

35

One Battleship

Two Destroyers

Three Submarines

Four Gunboats   **Miss**

BATTLESHIPS

We have hidden a fleet of ships in the grid. They have been placed horizontally or vertically, but they are never touching each other, not even diagonally. The numbers to the left or above indicate how many parts of ships can be found in that row or column. We've given you four hits and two misses to start you off.

Match the correct silhouette to the picture in the middle.

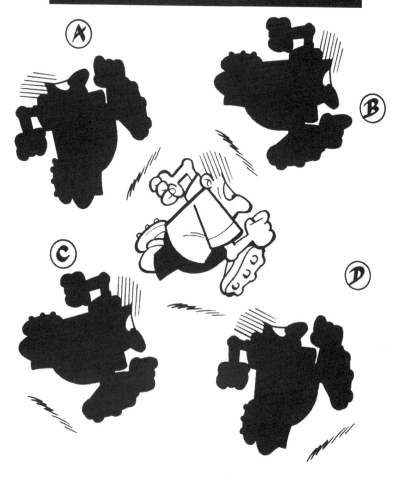

SAME SHELLS

Which two shells are identical?

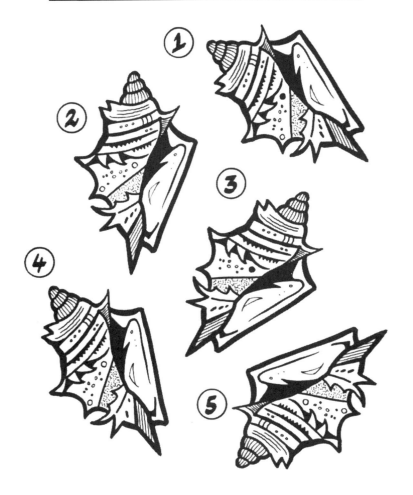

LETTER LETTER

Who is the letter from?
Shade in the dotted areas to find out.

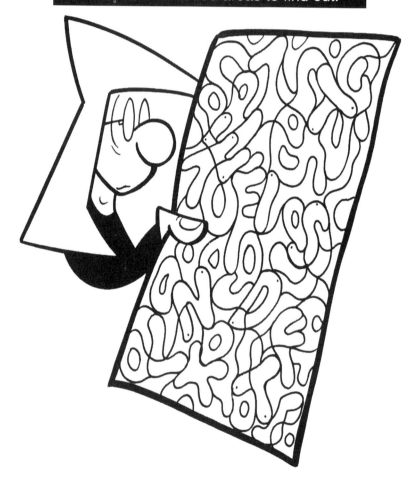

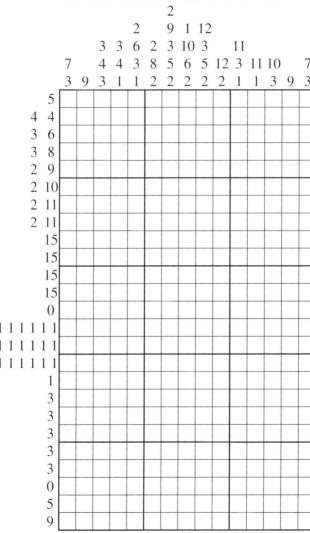

For instructions, see page 17

CHIEF PROBLEM

Which picture is the odd one out?

Can you spot 8 differences in the bottom picture?

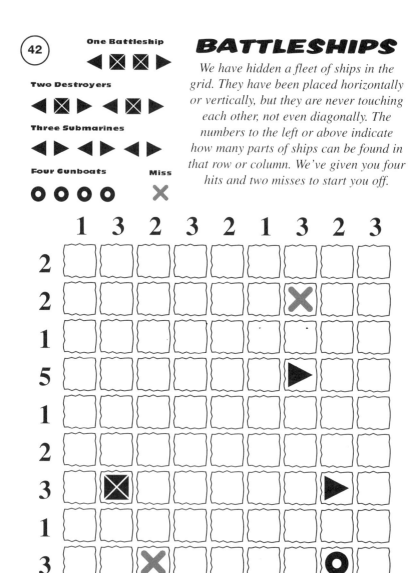

BATTLESHIPS

We have hidden a fleet of ships in the grid. They have been placed horizontally or vertically, but they are never touching each other, not even diagonally. The numbers to the left or above indicate how many parts of ships can be found in that row or column. We've given you four hits and two misses to start you off.

42

One Battleship

Two Destroyers

Three Submarines

Four Gunboats

Miss

HAIR CARE

Find a way through the maze to connect the hair dryer to the plug outlet.

SQUIDS IN!

Which silhouette exactly matches
the picture of the squid?

GET SHIRTY

Rearrange the letters to reveal the
surnames of five tennis players.

DVDilemma

Which DVD cover exactly matches the one the girl is holding?

What's at the window? Shade in the triangular shapes to find out!

SHOWER SCENE

Get rid of this rain shower by putting the pictures into their correct sequence.

BLOCKBUSTER

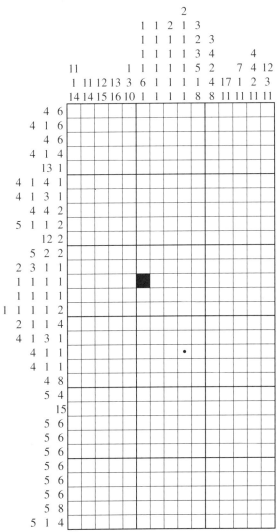

For instructions, see page 17

ODD SPACE

Which alien spaceship is the odd one out?

SPOT the DIFFERENCE

Can you spot 8 differences in the bottom picture?

One Battleship

Two Destroyers

Three Submarines

Four Gunboats   **Miss**

BATTLESHIPS

We have hidden a fleet of ships in the grid. They have been placed horizontally or vertically, but they are never touching each other, not even diagonally. The numbers to the left or above indicate how many parts of ships can be found in that row or column. We've given you four hits and two misses to start you off.

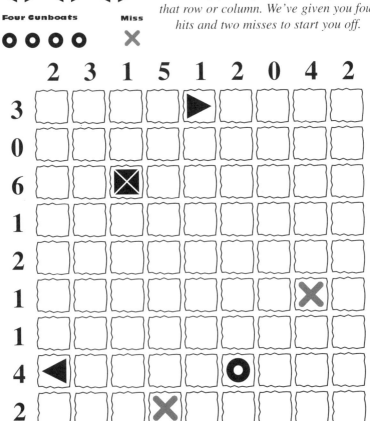

WORDSEARCH

We have hidden 15 different items, each beginning with the letter 'C' in the box of letters. Can you find them all in less than ten minutes?

```
Z R F H B C T T Z L N K
C O Q F D E B G G T W C
H A X J E L T S A C R U
G H M Q W L L J O O T Q
G H L E Y O D M W N C X
Y H N Q R D P N U D H W
B J X C H A I N A U A J
X J C P S E C J E C I D
T V T S I L S H U T R G
W N N W F I Z P U O D C
B K S H K D B N W R L R
U R W C S O O S T G C X
A L E M A C S O I F P H
O B Q R O O C L S Q V X
S Y D C R R D Z T Y P Y
J M G C N C U T C T G T
J T A Q Q D V A Q I V U
Z V E G O X F G D O B R
```

TREES & TENTS

(54)

*These tree and tent puzzles are straightforward to do,
just by following a few simple rules. Firstly, each tree in the grid
supports one tent, which must be in an adjacent square to the tree, to the
left, right, up or down, but not diagonally. In addition, no tent may be
adjacent to any other tent, either horizontally, vertically or diagonally.
The numbers along the rows and columns of the grid indicate the
number of tents in that row or column.*

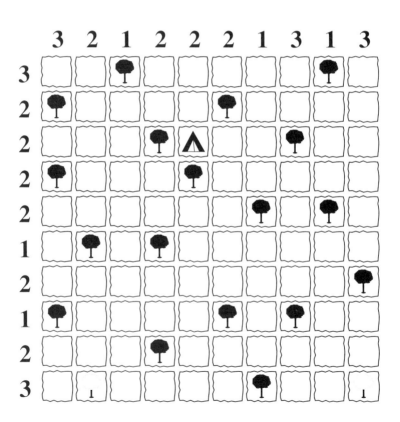

HATS OFF!

Rearrange the letters to reveal five kinds of hats or headwear.

1. STESO / TNE

2. MPANA / NAA

3. EAFRD / O

4. CLAA / LVBA / AA

5. CCLE / HO

LAVA FLOW

Which are the two matching volcanoes?

IN THE AIR

What is the girl looking at?
Shade in the triangular shapes to find out.

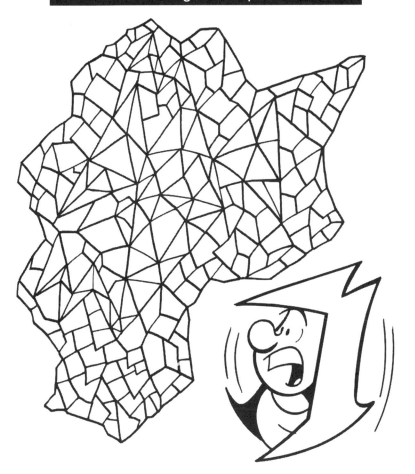

SPOT the SEQUENCE

Get rid of the girl's spots by putting the pictures into their correct sequence.

BLOCKBUSTER

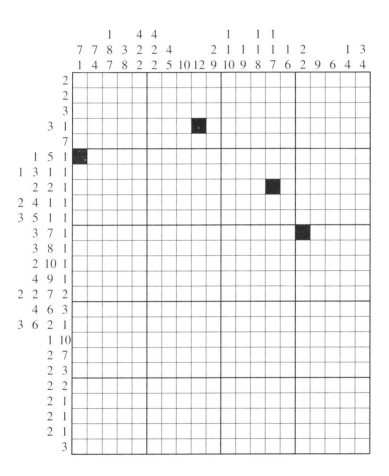

For instructions, see page 17
Turn on its side to see final picture

TRICK SHOT!

Find a way from the cue ball through the maze, to knock the black ball into the pocket.

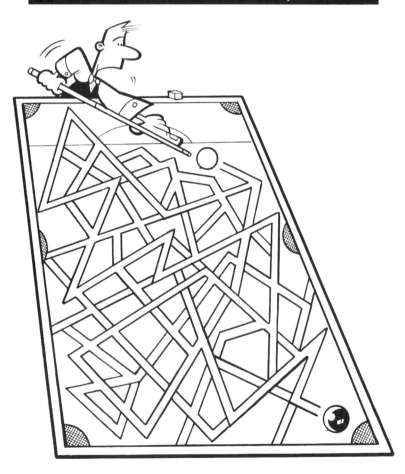

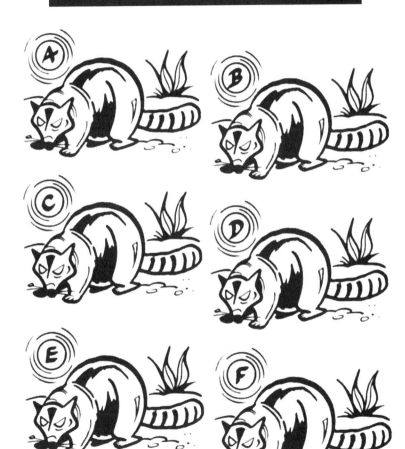

RACCOON RIDDLE

Which raccoon is the odd one out?

Find 8 differences in the bottom picture

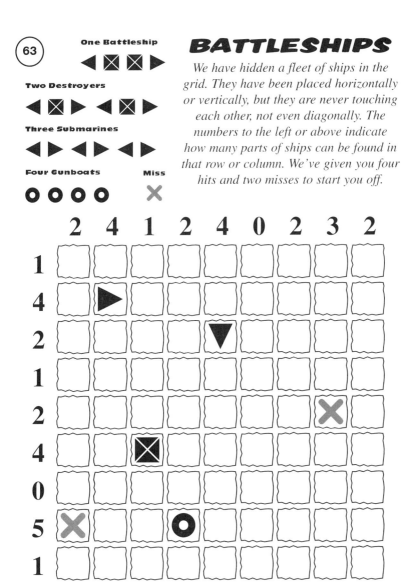

(63)

One Battleship

Two Destroyers

Three Submarines

Four Gunboats   **Miss**

BATTLESHIPS

We have hidden a fleet of ships in the grid. They have been placed horizontally or vertically, but they are never touching each other, not even diagonally. The numbers to the left or above indicate how many parts of ships can be found in that row or column. We've given you four hits and two misses to start you off.

	2	4	1	2	4	0	2	3	2
1									
4		▶							
2				▼					
1									
2									✕
4			⊠						
0									
5	✕			⊙					
1									

PUB CRAWL

Stagger your way through the maze to lead
this man home!

BIRD BRAIN

Which silhouette exactly matches the picture of the bird?

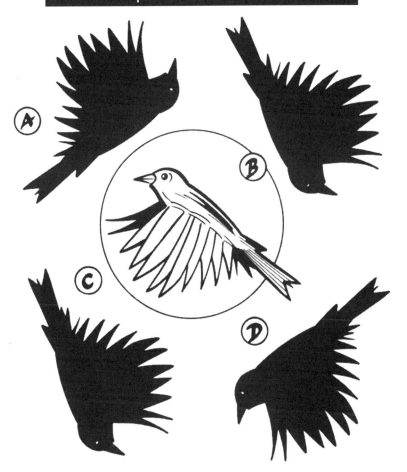

There are 10 diamonds hidden in this cave.
Can you find them?

NEWS FLASH

Rearrange the letters to reveal the names of five film stars in the news.

MATCH UP

Which picture on the left matches
one on the right?

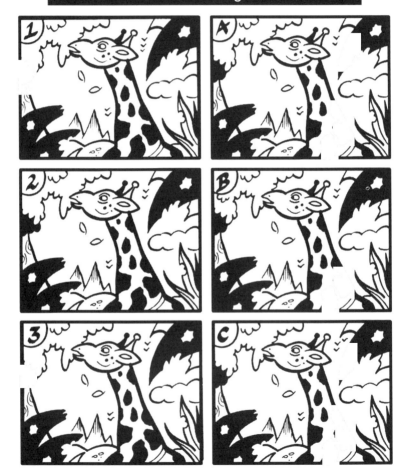

EYE TEST

Which letters are on the eye chart?
Shade in the dotted areas to find out.

STAR PAIR

Which two starfish are identical?

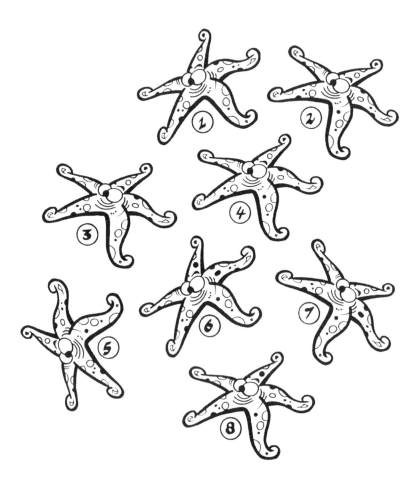

SHIP SHAPE

Put the pictures of the sinking ship into the correct sequence.

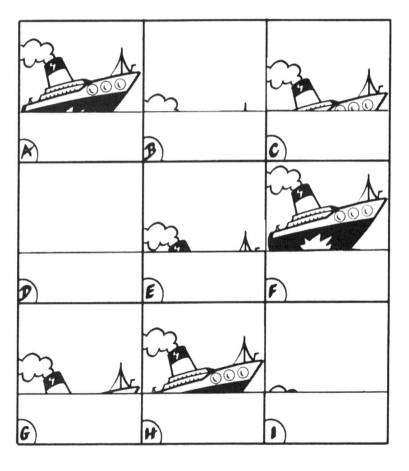

WORDSEARCH

We have hidden 15 different items, each beginning with the letter 'G' in the box of letters. Can you find them all in less than ten minutes?

```
E B V V J N L G T O A F
K Q L G O N D O L A R K
B U T R G Z G I Q O F V
A V Y A R H L C Y C B R
O P R S O F M H Z L X E
G C O S E G I O L A E E
L R T H Y S R V A A V J
O Q A O O S S I O T T T
V Z I P E M W A V G X V
E H D P E C P L L D S B
T O A E L F E B M G V R
A R L R L O R N Y M A V
G C G Y E G M U F T P H
L Y M N Z A L L I R O G
H N E K A W T U X T W O
T D G L G E G D E Q O R
D Y T I H C B P R M S O
S E P A R G O R B A L W
```

LAWN CARE

Lead the mower to the other end of the garden, carefully avoiding the 'objects' left by the dog!

TREES & TENTS

*These tree and tent puzzles are straightforward to do,
just by following a few simple rules. Firstly, each tree in the grid
supports one tent, which must be in an adjacent square to the tree, to the
left, right, up or down, but not diagonally. In addition, no tent may be
adjacent to any other tent, either horizontally, vertically or diagonally.
The numbers along the rows and columns of the grid indicate the
number of tents in that row or column.*

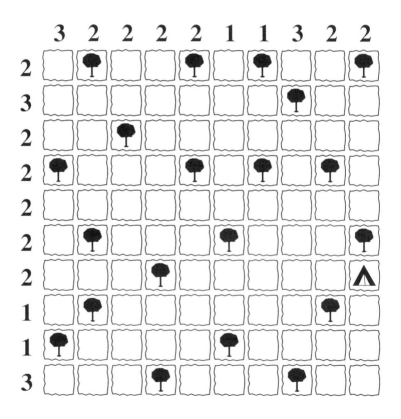

SPOT the DIFFERENCE

Find 8 differences in the bottom picture.

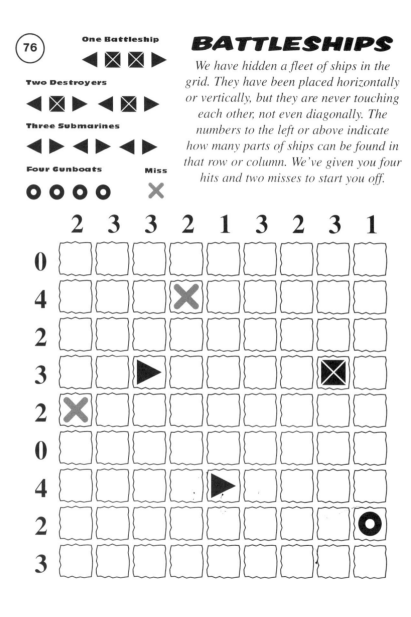

One Battleship

Two Destroyers

Three Submarines

Four Gunboats   **Miss**

BATTLESHIPS

We have hidden a fleet of ships in the grid. They have been placed horizontally or vertically, but they are never touching each other, not even diagonally. The numbers to the left or above indicate how many parts of ships can be found in that row or column. We've given you four hits and two misses to start you off.

BULLSEYE!

Find a way through the grid maze to lead the dart to the dartboard.

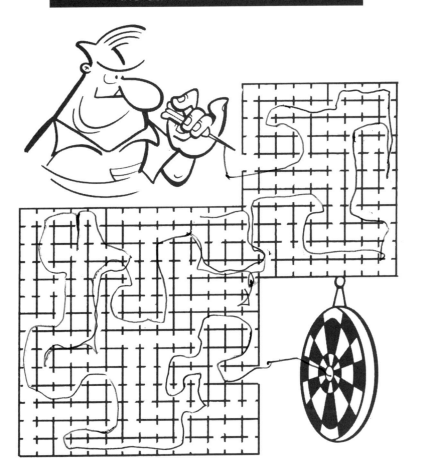

BAD APPLE

Which silhouette exactly matches the picture of the worm - filled apple?

STAR TREK

Can you find 10 stars hidden
somewhere in the picture?

PLANET WATCH

In each case, take the letters that are missing from the alphabet, then rearrange them to reveal the four planets the astronomer is looking at.

TOOTH MISSING

Can you spot the small detail missing
from each of these 8 pictures?

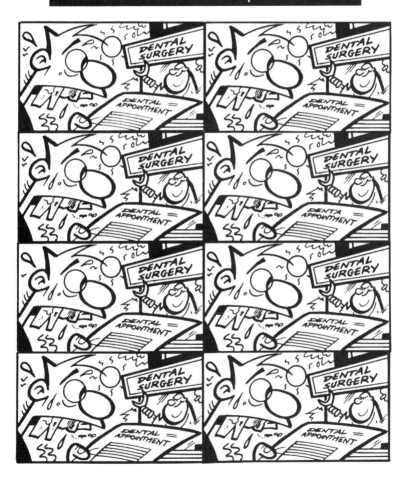

BASKET CASE

Something in the basket has scared off this woman.
Shade in the dotted areas to find out what it is!

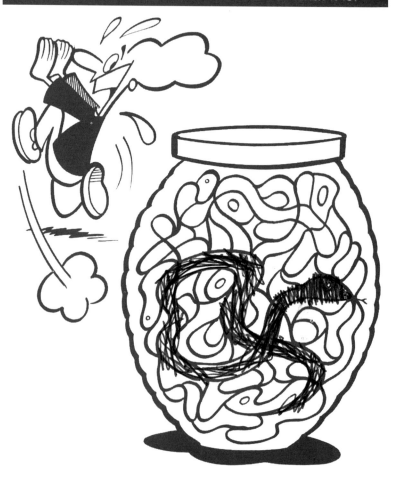

CROSSED WIRES

Which CD walkman is the girl listening to?

SNOWBUILDER

Put the building of this snowman into its correct order.

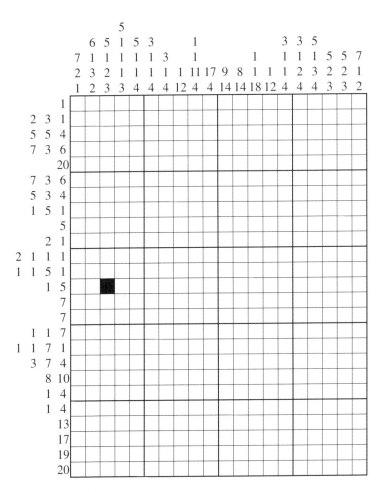

For instructions, see page 17

FORE!

Find a way through the grid maze, to lead the golf ball into the hole.

RAGING BULL

Which bull is the odd one out?

Find 8 differences in the bottom picture.

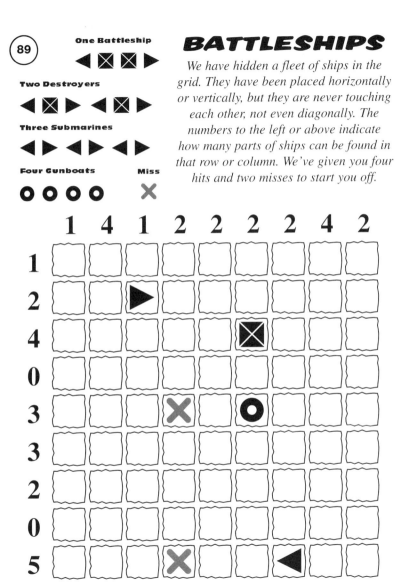

89

One Battleship

Two Destroyers

Three Submarines

Four Gunboats   **Miss**

BATTLESHIPS

We have hidden a fleet of ships in the grid. They have been placed horizontally or vertically, but they are never touching each other, not even diagonally. The numbers to the left or above indicate how many parts of ships can be found in that row or column. We've given you four hits and two misses to start you off.

RAZOR MAZE

Find a way through the grid maze to lead this man to his razor!

GHOST GUESS

Which silhouette exactly matches the picture of the ghost?

NEST EGG

How many eggs are there in the nest?

Rearrange the letters in each case to reveal the titles of five TV programmes.

DOUBLE TROUBLE

Only two of these girls are identical twins.
Which two?

BOX CLEVER

Shade in the triangular areas to find out what's in the box.

BUBBLE TROUBLE

Put the pictures of the girl blowing the
bubble into their correct sequence.

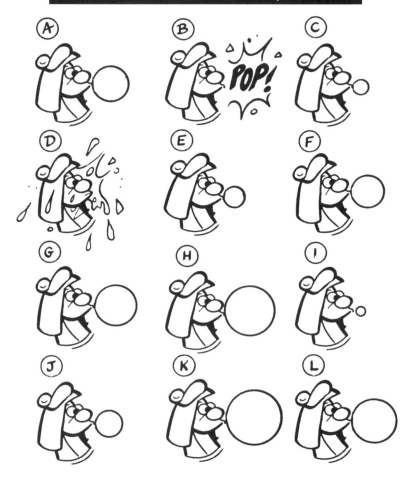

We have hidden 15 different items, each beginning with the letter 'P' in the box of letters. Can you find them all in less than ten minutes?

```
O G J W M U G A T Z J E
N I H V J P T H V W P H
W T P I N E A P P L E M
O N O O U A I A N O W I
X D O H G R B R N K Q L
G E D P A O O G T F P P
L O L T N C S O R L P W
P F E Y P J X T T H D V
K I Z O M U P O I G T F
C N P H V E M H E C P N
Q L I E K W O P Z W K Q
C L W L A H O X K X O P
T E P E N C I L U I K E
X J W N S Z O I L A N L
D W G I O T J C P I R I
Y S R B S I D A K T P C
H E F I O G J N C Z E A
P Q P T L L M E F Q W N
```

FEELING FLUSHED

Which man in the bathroom is the odd one out?

MISSING LINKS

Circle the small detail that is missing from each of the pictures.

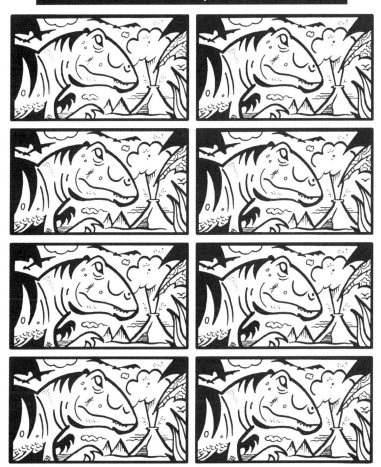

Find 8 differences in the bottom picture.

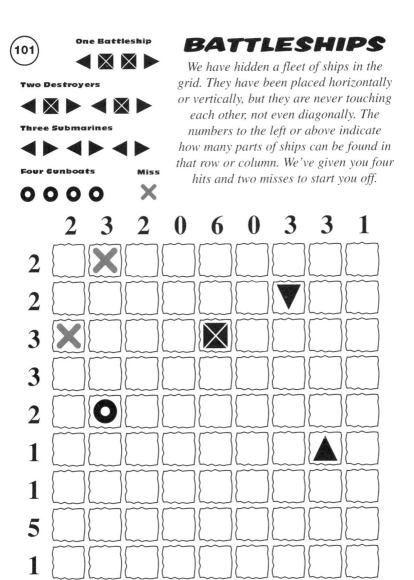

One Battleship

Two Destroyers

Three Submarines

Four Gunboats   **Miss**

BATTLESHIPS

We have hidden a fleet of ships in the grid. They have been placed horizontally or vertically, but they are never touching each other, not even diagonally. The numbers to the left or above indicate how many parts of ships can be found in that row or column. We've given you four hits and two misses to start you off.

CLEAN UP

Find a way through the grid maze to
help the cleaner find the window!

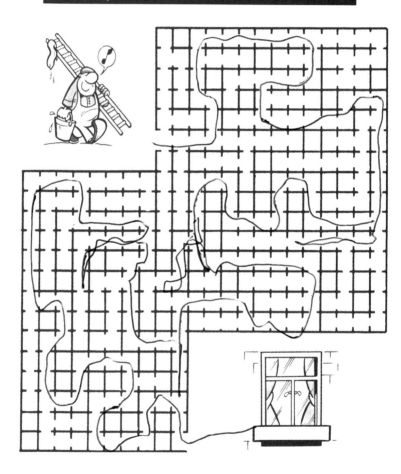

RIP-OFF!

Which is the missing piece of the punk's ripped T-shirt?

TREES & TENTS

*These tree and tent puzzles are straightforward to do,
just by following a few simple rules. Firstly, each tree in the grid
supports one tent, which must be in an adjacent square to the tree, to the
left, right, up or down, but not diagonally. In addition, no tent may be
adjacent to any other tent, either horizontally, vertically or diagonally.
The numbers along the rows and columns of the grid indicate the
number of tents in that row or column.*

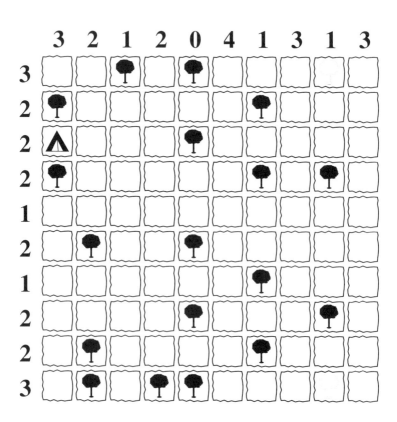

IN THE SOUP

Rearrange the letters to reveal six kinds of soup.

SKULLDUGGERY!

Which two of these skulls are identical?

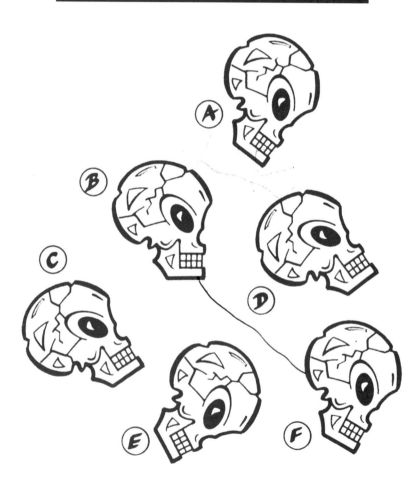

WONDERWALL

What's behind the wall? Shade in the triangular areas to find out.

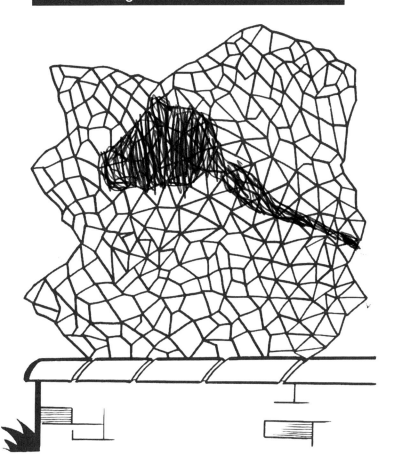

Which hearing aid is this dear old lady plugged into?

PRINTED!

Only one of these fingerprints is an exact match of this man's, which one?

WORDSEARCH

We have hidden 15 different items, each beginning with the letter 'B' in the box of letters. Can you find them all in less than ten minutes?

```
O G F D B Z T G W J N C
U L I A Z B K O A R G Q
H Q P E P A W B K Y M M
T R P B E G P O B I M A
P R Q L S P R N R U L B
H C B A N I R E L L A B
U Y K C N P T Y E T B O
C G O K L E R B H E R T
I D O B M S B A S K E T
F U M O L U P L E C S L
R C R A B K V L R U M E
E A E R U H C O R B M B
B V Y D U Y D O A J S H
O K B J C K L N B U A J
M A H I M E A W X W F X
T J B O J N A B L D P G
A K K R A E E D I F J S
N H L K P C N P I N I G
```

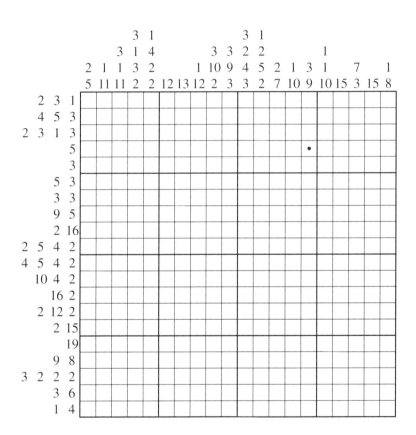

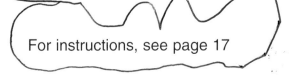

For instructions, see page 17

HEAD START

Find a way through the maze of hair

KOALA CHOICE

Which cuddly koala is the odd one out?

Can you spot 8 differences in the bottom picture?

(115)

One Battleship

◄ ⊠ ⊠ ►

Two Destroyers

◄ ⊠ ► ◄ ⊠ ►

Three Submarines

◄ ► ◄ ► ◄ ►

Four Gunboats　　**Miss**

● ● ● ●　　✕

BATTLESHIPS

We have hidden a fleet of ships in the grid. They have been placed horizontally or vertically, but they are never touching each other, not even diagonally. The numbers to the left or above indicate how many parts of ships can be found in that row or column. We've given you four hits and two misses to start you off.

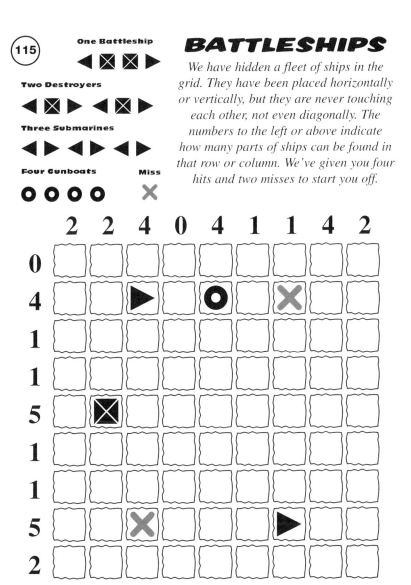

COFFEE BREAK

Find a way through the grid maze to let this woman have her coffee.

CRACKED!

Which is the missing piece of the broken vase?

RING-PULL RIDDLE

Find 8 ring-pulls in the picture below.

FISHY

Find the names of five oceans and seas in the bubble chain.

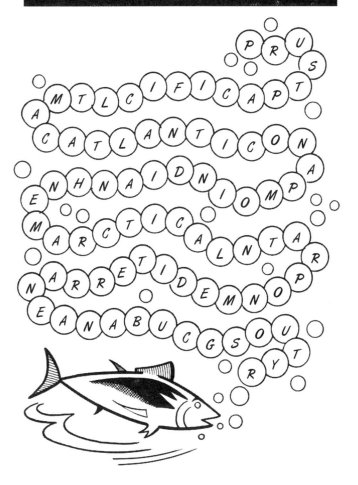

'B' PICTURES

Which two bugs are identical?

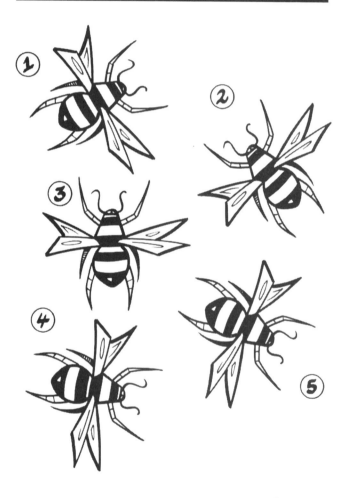

SKY VIEW

What's in the sky? Shade the areas
with two dots to find out.

MOUSE MAZE

Which 'mouse' is connected to the computer?

We have hidden 15 different items, each beginning with the letter 'H' in the box of letters. Can you find them all in less than ten minutes?

```
H Q C H D C M C I S T Z
H I Y A A W Y F B J M D
D O M M K M S I O Y V H
Q K V M W E P O M I A I
W H G E T H A E V I H K
Y J F R R L R J R I R F
G J I B D C L B H H R H
M N S A G G R H K R J H
V Y D H M U X A Y R E R
N I G W S T Y R F E E B
P U Q H V W Z P T T N A
W D D G M U U H S P Z A
H R R O A H M L R O O A
L E A D U B O D V C Q N
X A R T Z H D U M I E F
X Y G O F H W N S L Z T
C K Y H N R E T A E H B
R S F F U C D N A H I O
```

BLOCKBUSTER

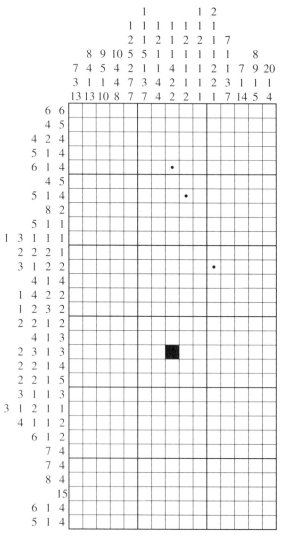

For instructions, see page 17

CROSSED LINES

Find a way through the maze,
to link up these two mobiles.

Which picture is the odd one out?

Find 8 differences in the bottom picture.

One Battleship

◀ ⊠ ⊠ ▶

Two Destroyers

◀ ⊠ ▶   ◀ ⊠ ▶

Three Submarines

◀ ▶   ◀ ▶   ◀ ▶

Four Gunboats   **Miss**

● ● ● ●   ✕

BATTLESHIPS

We have hidden a fleet of ships in the grid. They have been placed horizontally or vertically, but they are never touching each other, not even diagonally. The numbers to the left or above indicate how many parts of ships can be found in that row or column. We've given you four hits and two misses to start you off.

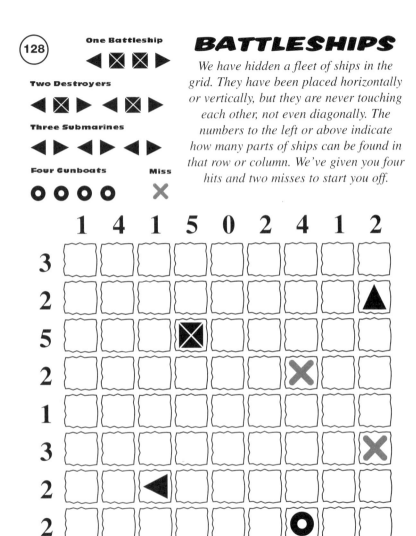

LOST ORDERS

Find a way through the maze to lead this man to his beer.

BEETLEMANIA!

Which silhouette exactly matches
the picture of the beetle?

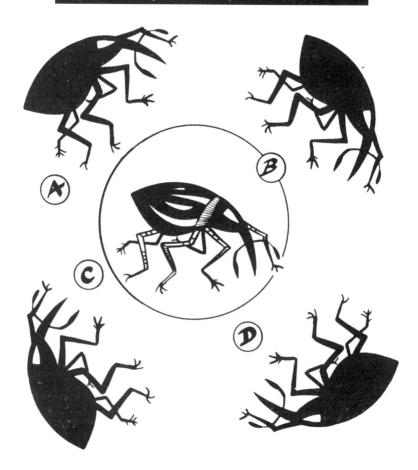

FLAT BATTERIES

Find 8 batteries for the CD walkman in the picture.

BOOT CHANGE

Can you change HEAD to BOOT in five moves, by changing one letter at a time?

TAKE AWAY

Which two pictures are identical?

IN THE BAG

**What's in the bag?
Shade in the triangles to find out.**

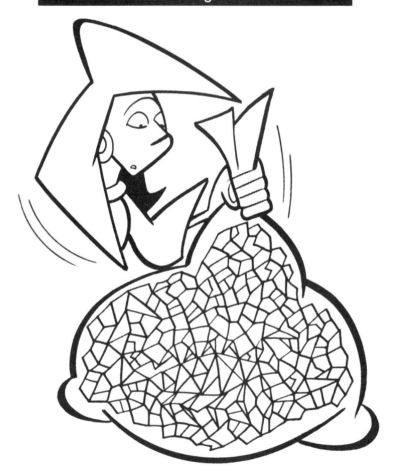

BAD HAIR DAY

Which lead plugs into the hair dryer?

CLOSE SHAVE

Put the pictures of this man shaving off his beard into their correct sequence.

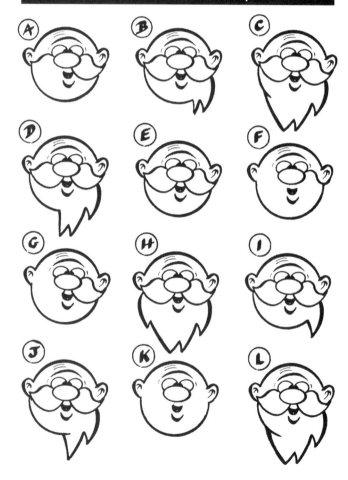

BLOCKBUSTER

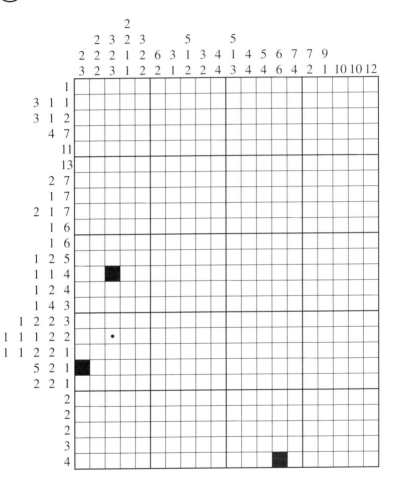

For instructions, see page 17

BRUSH UP

Find a way through the maze, to put the toothpaste on the toothbrush.

POLAR PUZZLE

Which polar bear is the odd one out?

Can you spot 8 differences in the bottom picture?

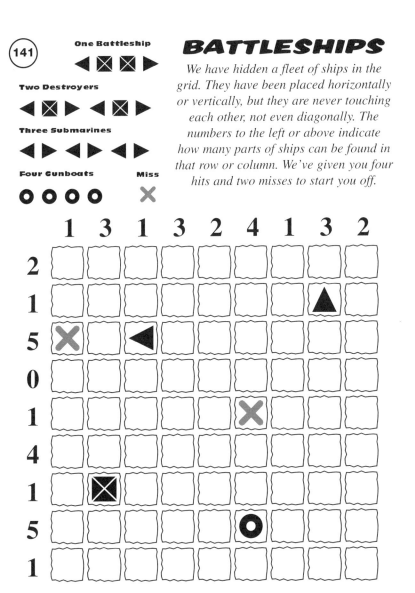

One Battleship

Two Destroyers

Three Submarines

Four Gunboats   **Miss**

BATTLESHIPS

We have hidden a fleet of ships in the grid. They have been placed horizontally or vertically, but they are never touching each other, not even diagonally. The numbers to the left or above indicate how many parts of ships can be found in that row or column. We've given you four hits and two misses to start you off.

	1	3	1	3	2	4	1	3	2
2									
1								▲	
5	✕		◀						
0									
1						✕			
4									
1		⊠							
5						◯			
1									

Find a way through the maze to lead the parachutist safely onto the target.

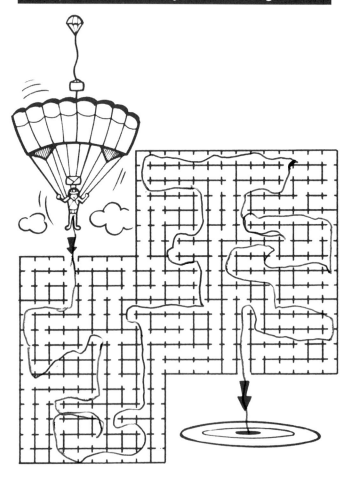

WHICH WHALE?

Which silhouette exactly matches the picture of the whale?

COMPUTER CRASH

This secretary's computer has crashed - so it looks like she'll have to use pencil and paper! Find her 8 pencils hidden in the picture.

Rearrange the letters in each case, to reveal five types of shop.

FISHING FOR CLUES

The picture at the top left is complete. Circle what is missing from the remaining seven pictures.

ROCK FORMATION

What's under the rock?
Shade in the triangles to find out.

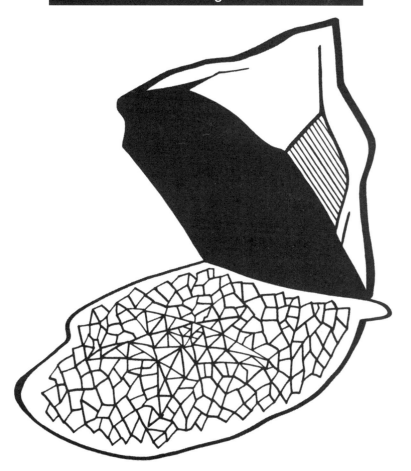

WONDERWOOL!

Which colour of wool is Granny Smith
knitting with? RED

CORE PROBLEM

Put the pictures of this lady eating her apple into their correct sequence.

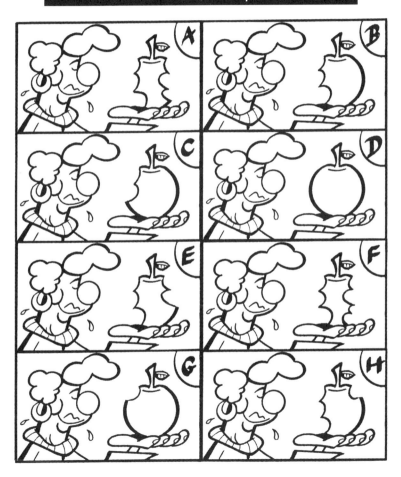

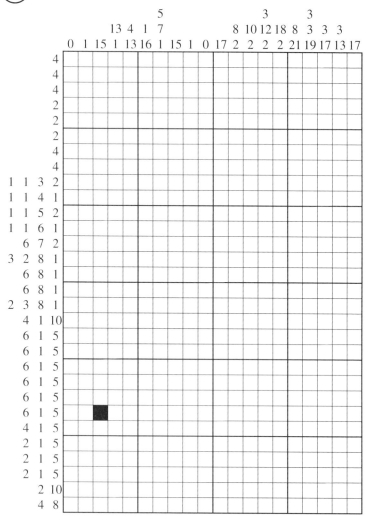

For instructions, see page 17

FLY SPRAY

Find a way through the maze
of spray, to zap the fly!

SPHINX LINKS

Which sphinx is the odd one out?

Can you spot 8 differences in the bottom picture?

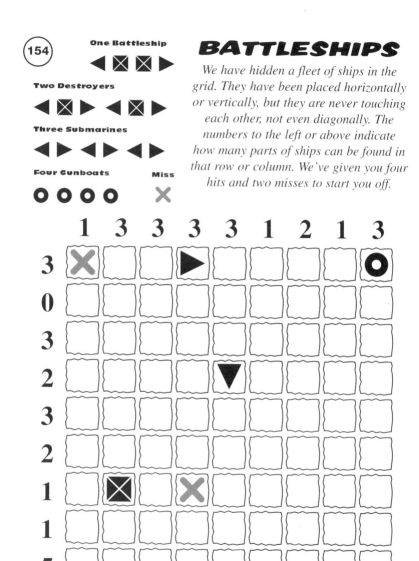

(154)

One Battleship

Two Destroyers

Three Submarines

Four Gunboats   **Miss**

BATTLESHIPS

We have hidden a fleet of ships in the grid. They have been placed horizontally or vertically, but they are never touching each other, not even diagonally. The numbers to the left or above indicate how many parts of ships can be found in that row or column. We've given you four hits and two misses to start you off.

MONGREL MAZE

Find a way through the grid maze, to lead the dog to the tree!

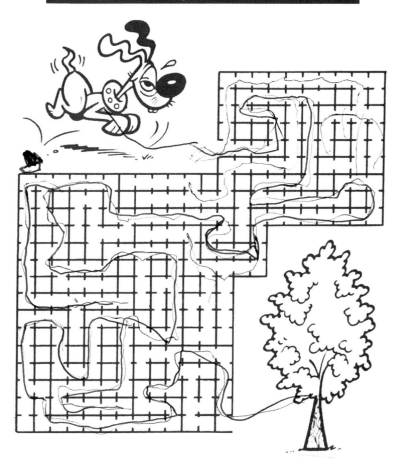

ROOT PROBLEM

Which silhouette exactly matches the picture of the radish?

A PIZZA THE ACTION!

Find ten mushrooms in the giant pizza.

CHOICE CUTS

Which two pieces of puzzle are not used in the main picture?

DOOR TO DOOR

Through each of these doors is a member of the medical profession. Rearrange the letters to reveal each one.

SQUARE DEAL

Using the grid reference, work out where each of these squares features in the picture.

PARTY PIECES

Circle what piece of each picture is missing.

What picture has this man drawn?
Shade in the triangles to find out.

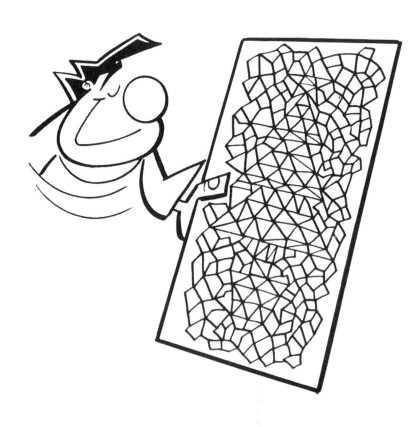

WORDSEARCH

We have hidden 15 different items, each beginning with the letter 'D' in the box of letters. Can you find them all in less than ten minutes?

```
G H X D V G U Q R Q X W
P Y P H T O X O G O D G
Q W L P C K K L I V M L
R I A A S H H U U Z U I
Z Y I E P Q M A Z H R V
D P D M H D N D J U D U
Q D W B R M R I V A O K
D M A I O E C C R Q U Q
S S L R S X V T B Z G Q
T L U S N M B I V I H H
Y K C U D O L O D Z N B
W Z A N A K G N K M U E
L I R R U T B A Y A T Q
V B D R A W E R R H X T
G K O R L Q Q Y A D C T
I U P M E K D L I O V V
Q S B U N G V P D V J O
T Z R W G D T T L E T V
```

Put the clown putting on his make-up into the correct sequence

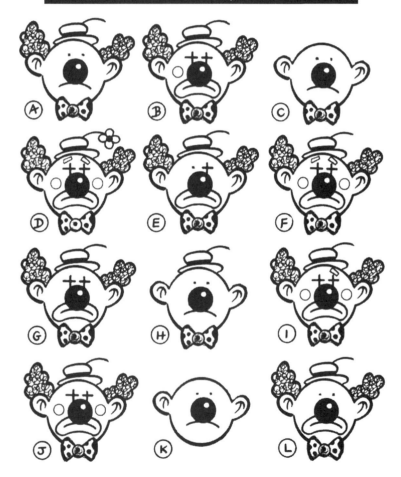

BLOCKBUSTER

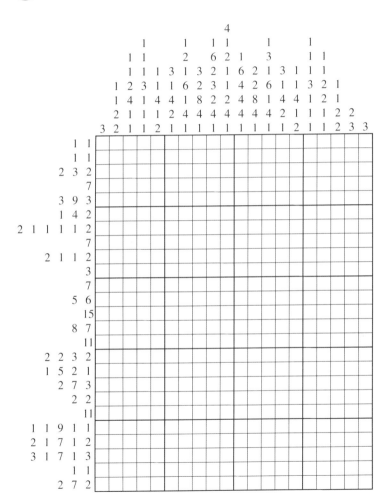

For instructions, see page 17

HONEY BEE

Find a way through the maze, to lead the
bee to the jar of honey.

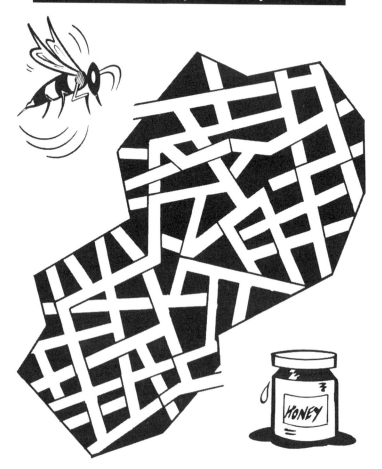

HEN-PICKED!

Pick out the hen that is the odd one out.

Can you spot 8 differences in the bottom picture?

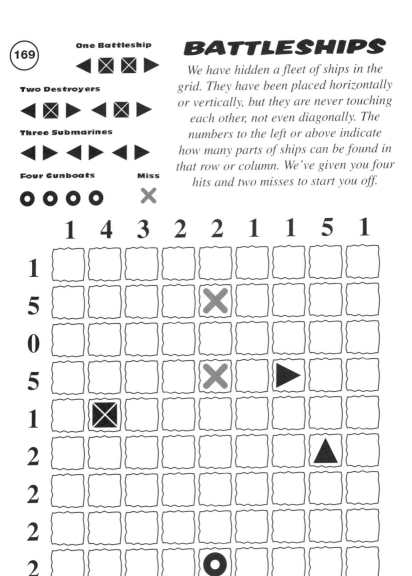

(169)

One Battleship

◀ ⊠ ⊠ ▶

Two Destroyers

◀ ⊠ ▶   ◀ ⊠ ▶

Three Submarines

◀ ▶   ◀ ▶   ◀ ▶

Four Gunboats   **Miss**

● ● ● ●   ✕

BATTLESHIPS

We have hidden a fleet of ships in the grid. They have been placed horizontally or vertically, but they are never touching each other, not even diagonally. The numbers to the left or above indicate how many parts of ships can be found in that row or column. We've given you four hits and two misses to start you off.

CAR TROUBLE

Get the car topped up before it runs out of gas!

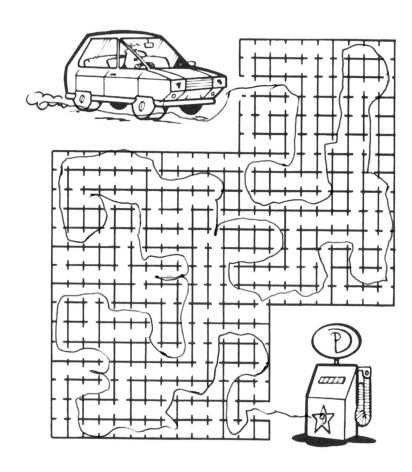

We have hidden 15 different items, each beginning with the letter 'A' in the box of letters. Can you find them all in less than ten minutes?

```
L E G N A M S U O L O U
C Z Y L F C U Z C D V U
P G H M H N P A K G V N
D A X B E I X T T U O A
U J L T N N M L E E R Q
A P P L E G Z A T M R Z
P H Z S I R L S C S L I
Y Q F R L G A H M P I Q
U K X Q A B A C U S V T
X A N D P I R T W S N B
P A N B R M D X O O A Q
D X I O Z D V P I R S V
H B W O R R A D J T I W
O T C X O A R T S A Z J
C P H L H O K C W B N K
M H J U C Z J S G L U G
N A A C N Z G M I A P Z
T L A L A R M C L O C K
```

SEA SEARCH

Find eight shark's teeth in the picture below
(not including the ones in its mouth!)

BAD BREAK

Which is the broken piece of the tennis racket?

POSTMARKS

Rearrange the letters to reveal the seven countries the letters are destined for.

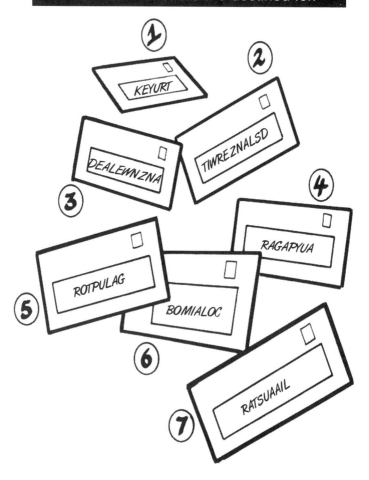

1. KEYURT
2. TIWREZNALSD
3. DEALEWNZNA
4. RAGAPYUA
5. ROTPULAG
6. BOMIALOC
7. RATSUAAIL

SOLUTIONS

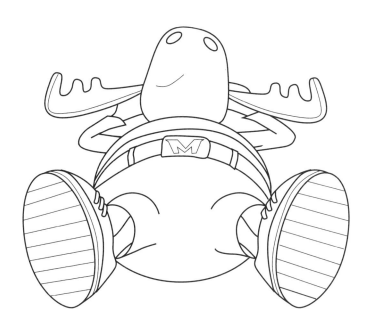

SOLUTIONS

1 - B&E

2 - 6

3 - B

4 - E&B

5 - C

6 -

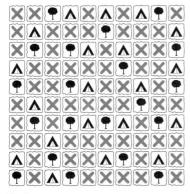

7 - C

8 - B&D

9 - F

10 -

11 - D

12 - 3&8

13 - 4

14 -

15 - 2

16 - A&F

17 -

SOLUTIONS

18 –

```
G Z X H F I F O C V Y L A
J S S H D B E J Q L T A D
E P D B Y L U E N Q X A E
W D I P M L P T A D A Y M
Z S M Q M O O N V I Y F Y
K Z X K U O S M S A F V L
C L F S M M F Q X M W L A
J A J A C M P F U R R C
H D Z M D M A G N E T D
M Q N Y P O I P Y M N T
A M I C R O P H O N E W
D A A X B S A O J L U W
B T T M U E R B L I G G
O A N N M H G A A Y B N
D D U E S O M B D D H J
T O O U U D T C S K E P
K R M Z L U Y H O C L C
M R L R O B A P T G K S
```

19 – E&C

20 –

21 –

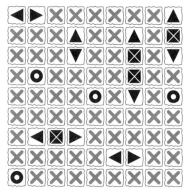

22 – A

23 – D

24 – MARMALADE

SOLUTIONS

25 -

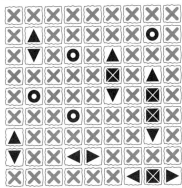

```
H W U E Y P Q D B G V F
H F C I O U B L T F Z J
H P H G J F T S E I F D
K I T C Q C I D N R R U
K J I Y A H O S F E Z K
B U I U P R K A H M V H
W M F T A L W T M A N Q
H M N S S T A H K N T U
Q F L O W E R U P H H N
K X E I F L A M I N G O
W Q N N F O U N T A I N
A S N L C N R Y S O L Y
E A U N A E Y T F P H
P Q F Y G Q A R B L S M
D J G N E U O E O A A U
U D I Y Z G G Z F Z L G
F B J Z R F E I W F L
X K R O W E R I F Z X G
```

26 - A

27 -

28 -

29 - A

30 - C&F

31 - MICHAEL

SOLUTIONS

32 -

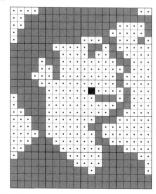

33 - 5

34 -

35 -

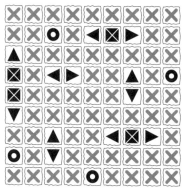

36 - C

37 - 2&5

38 - DENTIST

SOLUTIONS

39 -

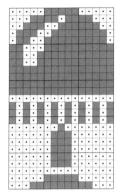

40 - E

41 -

42 -

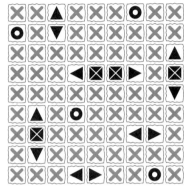

43 -

44 - A

45 - 1-Ivanisevic, 2-Williams,
3-Sampras, 4-Rusedski, 5-Capriati

46 - 3

SOLUTIONS

47 -

48 - H, C, J, D, I, B, G, A, F, K, E, L

49 -

50 - B

51 -

52 -

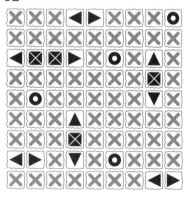

SOLUTIONS

53 -

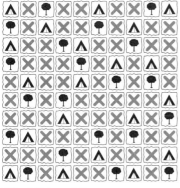

57 -

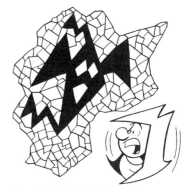

54 -

58 - G, B, K, I, A, H, F, L, D, J, C, E

59 -

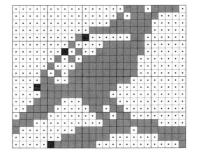

55 - 1-Stetson, 2-Panama,
3-Fedora, 4-Balaclava, 5-Cloche

56 - 2&7

SOLUTIONS

60 -

63 -

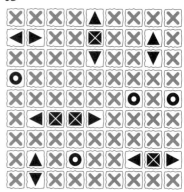

61 - D

62 -

64 -

65 - B

SOLUTIONS

66 -

67 - 1-Julia Roberts, 2-Sandra Bullock, 3-Sharon Stone, 4-Wesley Snipes, 5-Timothy Dalton

68 - 3&A

69 - C, L, S, D, X, T, O, A, P

70 - 2&5

71 - F, A, H, C, G, E, B, I, D

72 -

```
E B V V J N L G T O A F
K Q L G O N D O L A R K
B U T R G Z G I Q O F V
A V Y A R H L C Y C B R
O P R S O F M H Z L X E
G C O S E G I O L A E E
L R T H Y S R V A A V J
L O Q A O S S I O T T T
V Z I P E M W A V G X V
E H D P E C P L L D S B
T O A E L F E B M G V R
A R L R L O R N Y M A V
G C G Y E G M U F T P H
L Y M N Z A L L I R O G
H N E K A W T U X T W O
T D G L G E G D E Q O R
D Y T I H C B P R M S O
S E P A R G O R B A L W
```

73 -

SOLUTIONS

74 -

76 -

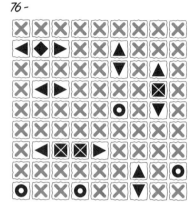

75 -

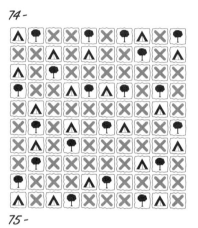

77 -

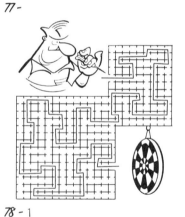

78 - 1

SOLUTIONS

79 -

80 - 1-Jupiter, 2-Saturn, 3-Venus, 4-Pluto

81 -

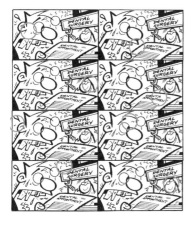

82 -

83 - B

84 - C, H, D, G, B, F, A, E

85 -

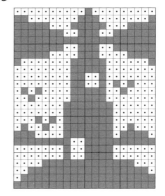

SOLUTIONS

86 -

87 - 5

88 -

89 -

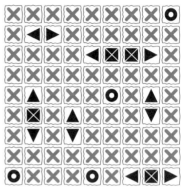

90 -

91 - A

92 - 26

93 - Starsky and Hutch,
The Dukes of Hazzard, Star Trek,
The Cosby Show, Friends.

SOLUTIONS

94 - C & E

95 -

96 - I, C, E, J, F, A, G, L, H, K, B, D

97 -

98 - 1

99 -

100 -

SOLUTIONS

101 -

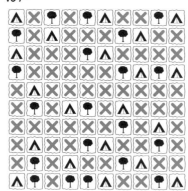

104 -

102 -

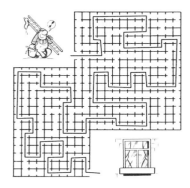

103 - 3

105 - 1-Minestrone, 2-Carrot and coriander, 3-Leek and potato, 4-Vegetable, 5-Chicken noodle, 6-French onion

106 - F&B

107 -

108 - 4

SOLUTIONS

109 - 6

110 -

```
O G F D B Z T G W J N C
U L I A Z B K O A R G Q
H Q P E P A W B K Y M M
T R P B E G P O B I M A
P R Q L S P R N R U L B
H C B A N I R E L L A B
U Y K C N P T Y E T B O
C G O K L E R B H E R T
I D O B M S B A S K E T
F U M O L U P L E C S L
R C R A B K V L R U M E
E A E R U H C O R B M B
B V Y D U Y D O A J S H
O K B J C K L N B U A J
M A H I M E A W X W F X
T J B O J N A B L D P G
A K K R A E E D I F J S
N H L K P C N P I N I G
```

111 -

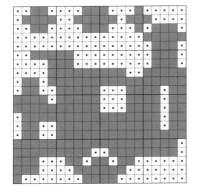

112 -

113 - B

114 -

SOLUTIONS

115 -

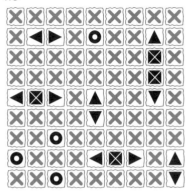

116 -

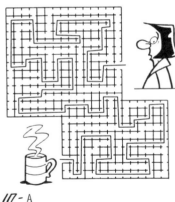

117 - A

118 -

119 -
Pacific, Atlantic, Indian, Arctic, Mediterranean

120 - 2&3

121 -

122 - 1

SOLUTIONS

123 -

```
H Q C H D C M C I S T Z
H I Y A W Y F B J M D
D O M M K M S I O Y V H
Q K V M W E P O M I A I
W H G E T H A E V I H K
Y J F R R L R J R I R F
G J I B D C L B H H R H
M N S A G G R H K R J H
V Y D H M U X A Y R E R
N I G W S T Y R F E E B
P U Q H V W Z P T T N A
W D D G M U U H S P Z A
H R R O A H M L R O O A
L E A D U B O D V C Q N
X A R T Z H D U M I E F
X Y G O F H W N S L Z T
C K Y H N R E T A E H B
R S F F U C D N A H I O
```

124 -

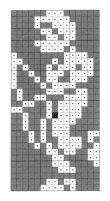

125 -

126 - BOTTOM RIGHT

127 -

SOLUTIONS

128 -

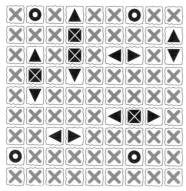

129 -

130 - D

131 -

132 - HEAD, HEAT, BEAT, BOAT, BOOT

133 - 3&7

134 -

135 - 3

136 - H, C, L, D, J, B, I, E, A, G, F, K

SOLUTIONS

137 -

140 -

138 -

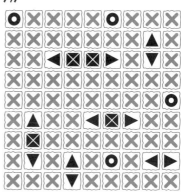

139 - MIDDLE LEFT

141 -

SOLUTIONS

142 -

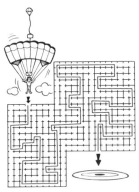

143 - C

144 -

145 - 1-Delicatessen, 2-Pharmacy,
3-Supermarket, 4-Haberdashery,
5-Stationers

146 -

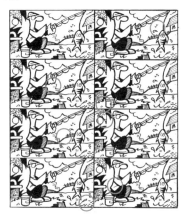

147 -

148 - RED
149 - D, G, C, B, H, E, A, F

SOLUTIONS

150 -

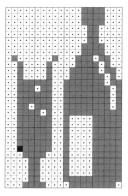

153 -

151 -

154 -

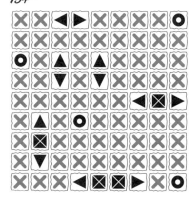

152 - E

SOLUTIONS

155 -

156 - 3

157 -

158 - A

159 - 1-Surgeon, 2-Optometrist,
3-Psychologist, 4-Orthodontist,
5-Physiotherapist

160 - 1 A-3, 2 C-4, 3 D-4, 4 D-1, 5 C-1,
6 B-3, 7 C-2, 8 A-5

161 -

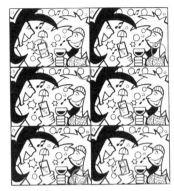

162 -

SOLUTIONS

163 -

```
G H X D V G U Q R Q X W
P Y P H T O X O G O D G
Q W L P C K K L I V M L
R I A A S H H U U Z U I
Z Y I E P Q M A Z H R V
D P D M H D N D J U D U
Q D W B R M R I V A O K
D M A I O E C C R Q U Q
S S L R S X V T B Z G Q
T L U S N M B I V I H H
Y K C U D O L O D Z N B
W Z A N A K G N K M U E
L I R R U T B A Y A T Q
V B D R A W E R R H X T
G K O R L Q Q Y A D C T
I U P M E K D L I O V V
Q S B U N G V P D V J O
T Z R W G D T T L E T V
```

164 - K, C, H, A, L, E, G, B, J, I, F, D

165 -

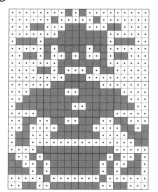

166 -

167 - 1

168 -

SOLUTIONS

169 -

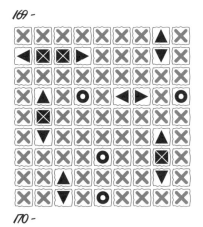

171 -

```
L E G N A M S U O L O U
C Z Y L F C U Z C D V U
P G H M H N P A K G V N
D A X B E I X T T U O A
U J L T N N M L E E R Q
A P P L E G Z A T M R Z
P H Z S I R L S C S L I
Y Q F R L G A H M P I Q
U K X Q A B A C U S V T
X A N D P I R T W S N B
P A N B R M D X O O A Q
D X I O Z D V P I R S V
H B W O R R A D J T I W
O T C X O A R T S A Z J
C P H L H O K C W B N K
M H J U C Z J S G L U G
N A A C N Z G M I A P Z
T L A L A R M C L O C K
```

170 -

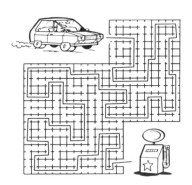

172 -

173 - C

174 - 1-Turkey, 2-Switzerland,
3-New Zealand, 4-Paraguay, 5-Portugal,
6-Colombia, 7-Australia

Other Books from Mad Moose Press

The Pocket Book of Golf Puzzles
(1-904139-07-8)

The Pocket Book of Pub Puzzles
(1-904139-08-6)

The Pocket Book of Travel Puzzles
(1-904139-09-4)

The Pocket Book of Mystery Movie Puzzles
(1-904139-10-8)

Close-up Puzzles
(1-904139-06-X)

mad
moose
press

Other Books from Mad Moose Press

The Pocket Book of Golf Puzzles
(1-904139-07-8)

The Pocket Book of Pub Puzzles
(1-904139-08-6)

The Pocket Book of Travel Puzzles
(1-904139-09-4)

The Pocket Book of Mystery Movie Puzzles
(1-904139-10-8)

Close-up Puzzles
(1-904139-06-X)